PRIMARY MATHEMATICS 5A
WORKBOOK

Marshall Cavendish
Education

SingaporeMath.com Inc®

Original edition published under the title Primary Mathematics Workbook 5A
© 1983 Curriculum Planning & Development Division
Ministry of Education, Singapore
Published by Times Media Private Limited
This American Edition
© 2003 Times Media Private Limited
© 2003 Marshall Cavendish International (Singapore) Private Limited

Published by Marshall Cavendish Education

An imprint of Marshall Cavendish International (Singapore) Private Limited
Times Centre, 1 New Industrial Road, Singapore 536196
Customer Service Hotline: (65) 6411 0820
E-mail: tmesales@sg.marshallcavendish.com
Website: www.marshallcavendish.com/education

SingaporeMath.com Inc®
Distributed by
SingaporeMath.com Inc
404 Beavercreek Road #225
Oregon City, OR 97045
U.S.A.
Website: www.singaporemath.com

First published 2003
Second impression 2003
Reprinted 2004 (twice)
Third impression 2005
Reprinted 2005, 2006 (thrice), 2007, 2008, 2009 (twice), 2010 (twice),
        2011, 2012 (twice)

ISBN 978-981-01-8512-1

Printed in Singapore by Times Printers, www.timesprinters.com

ACKNOWLEDGEMENTS

Our special thanks to Richard Askey, Professor of Mathematics (University of Wisconsin, Madison), Yoram Sagher, Professor of Mathematics (University of Illinois, Chicago), and Madge Goldman, President (Gabriella and Paul Rosenbaum Foundation), for their indispensable advice and suggestions in the production of Primary Mathematics (U.S. Edition).

CONTENTS

EXERCISE 1

1. Write the following in figures.

(a)	Twenty-four thousand, six hundred eight	
(b)	Sixteen thousand, eleven	
(c)	Ninety-nine thousand, nine	
(d)	Three hundred twelve thousand, four hundred sixty	
(e)	Eight hundred two thousand, three	
(f)	Five hundred forty thousand, fourteen	
(g)	Nine hundred thousand, nine hundred nine	

2. Write the following in words.

(a)	50,234	
(b)	26,008	
(c)	73,506	
(d)	367,450	
(e)	506,009	
(f)	430,016	
(g)	800,550	

3. Fill in the blanks.

   (a) In **27,685**, the digit **7** stands for _____.

   (b) In **61,260**, the digit _____ is in the **ten thousands** place.

   The value of the digit is _____.

   (c) In **432,091** the digit **0** is in the _____ place.

   (d) In **368,540**, the value of the digit **4** is _____.

Fill in the blanks.

4.   (a) $40,000 + 2000 + 100 + 8 =$ _____

        (b) $562,000 + 32 =$ _____

        (c) $700,000 + 70,000 + 70 + 7 =$ _____

        (d) $900,000 + 214 =$ _____

5.   (a) $25,830 = 25,000 +$ _____ $+ 30$

        (b) $370,049 =$ _____ $+ 70,000 + 40 + 9$

        (c) $603,804 = 600,000 +$ _____ $+ 800 + 4$

        (d) $416,008 = 416,000 +$ _____

6.   Complete the following number patterns.

        (a) $35,552,$ _____, _____, $38,552, \ 39,552$

        (b) $71,680, \ 71,780,$ _____, $71,980,$ _____

        (c) $28,361, \ 29,361,$ _____, _____, $32,361$

7.   (a) Which is greater, 13,268 or 31,862?   _____

        (b) Which is smaller, 49,650 or 42,650?   _____

        (c) Which is the greatest, 33,856, 33,786 or 33,796?   _____

        (d) Which is the smallest, 65,730, 65,703 or 66,730?   _____

8.   Rearrange each set of digits to make the greatest possible number and the smallest possible number.

	Greatest number	Smallest number
9, 6, 4, 1, 3		
1, 1, 6, 8, 7		

EXERCISE 2

1. Write the following in figures.

(a)	Three million	
(b)	Four million, one hundred fifty thousand	
(c)	Six million, thirty-one thousand	
(d)	Seven million, two hundred eight thousand	
(e)	Five million, five thousand	
(f)	Nine million, nine hundred nine thousand	
(g)	Ten million	

2. Write the following in words.

(a) 4,000,000

_____

(b) 3,040,000

_____

(c) 6,350,000

_____

(d) 5,006,000

_____

(e) 7,703,000

_____

(f) 9,099,000

_____

(g) 8,567,000

_____

3.

$1,000,000 $1000 $100 $1

$2,003,000

$100

$705

Write the total amount of money in figures: _____

In words, it is _____

4.   Rahman bought a house with this amount of money.

$1,000,000 $100,000

Write the price of the house in figures: _____

In words, it is _____

EXERCISE 3

Fill in the blanks.

1. (a)

297 is _____ when rounded off to the nearest ten.

(b)

1315 is _____ when rounded off to the nearest ten.

2. (a)

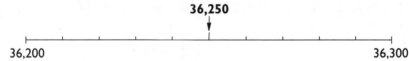

5982 is _____ when rounded off to the nearest hundred.

(b)

36,250 is _____ when rounded off to the nearest hundred.

3. (a)

46,120 is _____ when rounded off to the nearest thousand.

(b)

235,870 is _____ when rounded off to the nearest thousand.

4. Fill in the blanks.

```
|----+----+----+----+----+----+----+----|
244,000    245,000    246,000    247,000    248,000
```

(a) 245,230 is _____ when rounded off to the nearest thousand.

(b) 247,826 is _____ when rounded off to the nearest thousand.

5. (a) 43,192 is _____ when rounded off to the nearest ten.

(b) 14,563 is _____ when rounded off to the nearest hundred.

(c) 82,926 is _____ when rounded off to the nearest thousand.

(d) 196,425 is _____ when rounded off to the nearest thousand.

6. Round off each of the following to the nearest $100.

(a) $4385 _____   (b) $5250 _____

(c) $26,086 _____   (d) $39,745 _____

(e) $59,904 _____   (f) $62,263 _____

7. Round off each of the following to the nearest $1000.

(a) $3098 _____   (b) $5672 _____

(c) $18,296 _____   (d) $24,983 _____

(e) $43,825 _____   (f) $48,930 _____

(g) $328,500 _____   (h) $693,489 _____

10

EXERCISE 4

1.   Add.

(a) | $27{,}000 + 9000 =$
(b) | $8000 + 5000 =$
(c) | $32{,}000 + 8000 =$

2.   Subtract.

(a) | $53{,}000 - 4000 =$
(b) | $6000 - 2000 =$
(c) | $45{,}000 - 6000 =$

3.   Multiply.

(a) | $800 \times 2 =$
(b) | $500 \times 4 =$
(c) | $2000 \times 6 =$

4.   Divide.

(a) | $1800 \div 6 =$
(b) | $2400 \div 8 =$
(c) | $5600 \div 7 =$

5. Estimate the value of each of the following:

(a) $3064 + 5604 \approx 3000 + 6000$

$=$

(b) $4831 + 8205 \approx$

(c) $25,468 + 6925 \approx$

(d) $86,723 + 9207 \approx$

(e) $7356 - 3988 \approx$

(f) $9306 - 4568 \approx$

(g) $36,547 - 8865 \approx$

(h) $63,006 - 1008 \approx$

6. Estimate the value of each of the following:

(a) $3306 \times 2 \approx 3000 \times 2$

$= $

$3306 \approx 3000$

(b) $4811 \times 4 \approx$

(c) $8286 \times 6 \approx$

(d) $9560 \times 5 \approx$

(e) $6146 \div 3 \approx 6000 \div 3$

$= $

(f) $4759 \div 6 \approx$

(g) $5268 \div 5 \approx$

(h) $6398 \div 9 \approx$

EXERCISE 5

1. Multiply.

(a) $254 \times 10 =$	(b) $602 \times 100 =$
(c) $93 \times 40 =$	(d) $57 \times 1000 =$
(e) $43 \times 600 =$	(f) $392 \times 800 =$
(g) $72 \times 5000 =$	(h) $805 \times 3000 =$

2. Estimate the value of each of the following:

(a) $326 \times 47 \approx 300 \times 50$

   $=$

(b) $78 \times 586 \approx$

(c) $32 \times 705 \approx$

(d) $4165 \times 53 \approx$

3. Andrew wants to buy 28 radio sets. Each radio set costs $229. Give a quick estimate of the total cost of the radio sets.

4. Give a quick estimate of the area of a rectangle with length 114 in. and width 92 in.

EXERCISE 6

1. Divide.

(a) $360 \div 10 =$	(b) $4200 \div 100 =$
(c) $250 \div 50 =$	(d) $5600 \div 800 =$
(e) $1050 \div 70 =$	(f) $6000 \div 400 =$
(g) $63,000 \div 9000 =$	(h) $96,000 \div 6000 =$

2. Estimate the value of each of the following:

(a) $282 \div 52 \approx 300 \div 50$

$=$

(b) $324 \div 42 \approx$

(c) $4406 \div 49 \approx$

(d) $1705 \div 31 \approx$

3. Albert bought 28 compact discs for $805. Give a quick estimate of the cost of each compact disc.

4. The floor area of a hall is 1044 m². The length is 36 m. Give a quick estimate of the width of the hall.

EXERCISE 7

1. Find the value of each of the following:

(a) 48 + 12 + 37
 	
  =
	(b) 40 − 14 − 9
	
	  =

(c) 36 + 18 − 19
 	
  =
	(d) 51 − 35 + 18
	
	  =

(e) 7 × 5 × 8
 	
  =
	(f) 96 ÷ 3 ÷ 4
	
	  =

(g) 14 × 9 ÷ 3
 	
  =
	(h) 64 ÷ 8 × 5
	
	  =

2. Find the value of each of the following:

(a) $84 + 6 \times 8$ =	(b) $140 - 40 \times 3$ =
(c) $46 + 32 \div 8$ =	(d) $100 - 60 \div 4$ =
(e) $8 \times 6 + 14$ =	(f) $80 + 18 \div 6$ =
(g) $12 \times 10 - 5$ =	(h) $72 + 6 \times 6$ =

3. Find the value of each of the following:

(a) $70 + 24 \div 6 - 4$ =	(b) $125 \div 5 - 12 \times 2$ =
(c) $160 - 60 \div 4 \times 3$ =	(d) $32 + 8 + 30 \times 2$ =
(e) $52 - 35 \div 7 - 7 \times 2$ =	(f) $9 \times 8 - 6 \times 10$ =
(g) $7 \times 8 + 24 \div 8$ =	(h) $63 \div 9 + 20 \div 10$ =

EXERCISE 8

1. Find the value of each of the following:

(a) 69 + (46 − 15)
 	
  =
	(b) 90 − (24 + 36)
	
	  =

(c) 52 − (40 − 22)
 	
  =
	(d) (31 − 20) − 8
	
	  =

(e) 8 × (3 × 2)
 	
  =
	(f) 84 ÷ (4 ÷ 2)
	
	  =

(g) 9 × (20 ÷ 5)
 	
  =
	(h) 45 ÷ (15 × 3)
	
	  =

2. Find the value of each of the following:

(a) $(19 + 16) \div 5$ =	(b) $12 \times (9 - 4)$ =
(c) $64 \div (8 - 6)$ =	(d) $(14 + 6) \times 5$ =
(e) $10 \times (15 \div 5)$ =	(f) $(100 - 44) \div 7$ =
(g) $72 \div (9 - 3)$ =	(h) $(28 - 18) \times 10$ =

3. Find the value of each of the following:

(a) 20 + (8 + 4) ÷ 3
 	
   =
	(b) 16 + (9 − 3) × 5
	
	   =

(c) 7 × (4 + 2) × 8
 	
   =
	(d) 7 × (13 − 6) − 19
	
	   =

(e) 60 + (18 + 7) ÷ 5
 	
   =
	(f) 8 × (11 − 8) ÷ 6
	
	   =

(g) 24 ÷ 6 + 3 × (6 − 4)
 	
   =
	(h) 30 + (28 − 8) ÷ 5 × 2
	
	   =

EXERCISE 9

1. Elaine has 274 beads. 150 of them are blue, 70 are red and the rest are white. How many more red beads than white beads are there?

---

2. Tickets to a concert cost $15 per adult and $8 per child. Matthew bought tickets for 4 adults and 5 children. How much did he spend altogether?

3. At a carnival, Ann sold 314 bottles of drinks a day. She sold 66 bottles more in the afternoon than in the morning. How many bottles of drinks did she sell in the morning?

---

4. Adam bought a pen. He also bought a book which cost 3 times as much as the pen. He spent $112 altogether. Find the cost of the book.

EXERCISE 10

1. Chris paid $36 for 3 tank-tops and 2 T-shirts. A T-shirt cost 3 times as much as a tank-top. How much did Chris pay for the 2 T-shirts?

2. Peter bought 45 greeting cards at 3 for $2. He sold all of them at 5 for $4. How much money did he make?

3. A box of cookies cost $6 and a bottle of milk cost $2. After paying for 2 boxes of cookies and 6 bottles of milk, Nicole had $30 left. How much money did she have at first?

4. Lily and Sara each had an equal amount of money at first. After Lily spent $18 and Sara spent $25, Lily had twice as much as Sara. How much money did each have at first?

EXERCISE 11

1. Multiply.

(a) 78 × 40 =

$$\begin{array}{r} 78 \\ \times\ 40 \\ \hline \end{array}$$

(b) 46 × 50 =

(c) 53 × 24 =

(d) 65 × 89 =

(e) 246 × 70 =

(f) 309 × 60 =

(g) 508 × 32 =

(h) 760 × 87 =

2. Multiply.

(a) $1257 \times 30 =$ $\begin{array}{r} 1257 \\ \times \quad 30 \\ \hline \end{array}$	(b) $4008 \times 70 =$
(c) $1870 \times 20 =$	(d) $6229 \times 13 =$
(e) $3424 \times 25 =$	(f) $1003 \times 63 =$
(g) $1075 \times 73 =$	(h) $8207 \times 46 =$

EXERCISE 12

1. Divide.

<table>
<tr><td>(a) $60 \div 20 =$

$20\overline{)60}$</td><td>(b) $94 \div 30 =$</td></tr>
<tr><td>(c) $790 \div 80 =$</td><td>(d) $577 \div 90 =$</td></tr>
<tr><td>(e) $98 \div 32 =$</td><td>(f) $88 \div 49 =$</td></tr>
<tr><td>(g) $580 \div 64 =$</td><td>(h) $299 \div 53 =$</td></tr>
</table>

2. Divide.

(a) $92 \div 17 =$ $17\overline{)92}$	(b) $85 \div 22 =$
(c) $80 \div 26 =$	(d) $96 \div 34 =$
(e) $361 \div 62 =$	(f) $397 \div 47 =$
(g) $425 \div 54 =$	(h) $192 \div 38 =$

EXERCISE 13

1. Divide.

(a) $528 \div 30 =$ $30\overline{)528}$	(b) $820 \div 40 =$
(c) $307 \div 20 =$	(d) $650 \div 50 =$
(e) $485 \div 15 =$	(f) $700 \div 21 =$
(g) $820 \div 42 =$	(h) $908 \div 56 =$

2. Divide.

(a) 9963 ÷ 41 = $41\overline{)9963}$	(b) 8282 ÷ 16 =
(c) 6600 ÷ 55 =	(d) 9229 ÷ 29 =
(e) 2624 ÷ 32 =	(f) 5821 ÷ 63 =
(g) 7801 ÷ 48 =	(h) 3008 ÷ 25 =

REVIEW 1

Write the answers in the boxes.

1. Write the following in words.

   (a) 2044

   (b) 15,508

   (c) 376,920

   (d) 6,400,000

2. Write the following in figures.

   (a) Four thousand, eight

   (b) Twenty-seven thousand, three hundred

   (c) Sixty thousand, eleven

   (d) Two million, nine hundred four thousand

3. Find the value of each of the following:

   (a) 50,000 + 8000 + 30

   (b) 6,000,000 + 42,000 + 500

4. (a) In 8,453,000, the digit ☐ is in the hundred thousands place.

   (b) In 5,236,000, the digit 3 stands for 3 × ☐ .

34

5. (a) 8206 is 1000 more than ☐.

(b) 62,440 is 1000 less than ☐.

(c) 9345 is ☐ more than 9305.

(d) 7188 is ☐ less than 7988.

6. (a) Which is greater, 45,832 or 45,382? ☐

(b) Which is smaller, 30,012 or 30,102? ☐

7. Arrange the following numbers in decreasing order.

64,748, 76,435, 87,660, 60,083.

☐

8. (a) List all the factors of 24.

☐

(b) Write the first twelve multiples of 6.

☐

9. Which one of the following is the smallest?

90,786, 84,007, 91,000, 80,999 ☐

10. Find the value of each of the following:

(a) $145 - 25 \times 4$ ☐

(b) $228 \div 6 \times 2$ ☐

(c) $306 - 45 \div 9$ ☐

(d) $440 - 64 + 36 \div 6$ ☐

11. (a) 4 h 54 min = [   ] min

(b) 3 m 5 cm = [   ] cm

(c) 5 kg 500 g = [   ] g

(d) 2050 g = [   ] kg [   ] g

(e) 30 months = [   ] years [   ] months

12. (a) Round off 49,501 to the nearest hundred. [   ]

(b) Round off 49,501 to the nearest thousand. [   ]

13. (a) Find the sum of 12,099 and 900. [   ]

(b) Find the difference between 79 and 2100. [   ]

(c) Find the product of 540 and 28. [   ]

(d) Find the quotient and remainder when 127 is divided by 40. [   ]

14. 200 children took part in a concert. There were 4 times as many girls as boys.

(a) How many girls were there? [   ]

(b) How many more girls than boys were there? [   ]

15. Find the area of the figure. [   ]

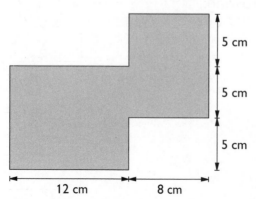

5 cm

5 cm

5 cm

12 cm   8 cm

36

16. The figure is made up of 2-cm squares.

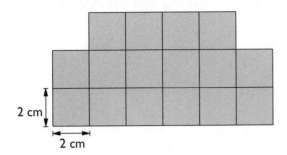

   (a) Find the area of the figure.

   (b) Find the perimeter of the figure.

17. Draw a straight line to divide the figure into two parts of equal area.

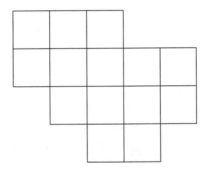

18. The figure is made up of two rectangles.

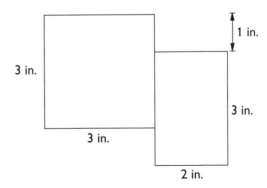

   (a) Find its area.

   (b) Find its perimeter.

19. Miguel had 45 melons. He sold 25 of them at $6 each. He sold the rest at $4 each. How much money did he receive?

20. Ashley bought a bed for $295. She also bought 2 mattresses at $65 each. She gave the cashier a $500 note. How much change did she receive?

21. Brandy has 278 stamps. Jane has 64 stamps more than Brandy. Sam and Jane have 500 stamps altogether. How many stamps does Sam have?

22. A rectangular piece of carpet is placed on the floor of a room leaving a margin 1 yd around it. The room measures 7 yd by 6 yd. Find the cost of the carpet if 1 yd^2 of it costs $75.

EXERCISE 14

1. Write each of the following as an improper fraction.

    (a)

    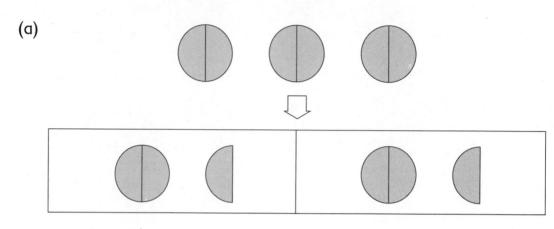

    $3 \div 2 =$

    (b)

    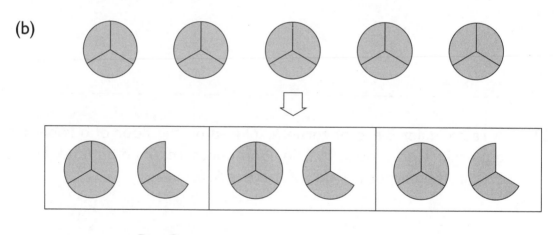

    $5 \div 3 =$

    (c)

    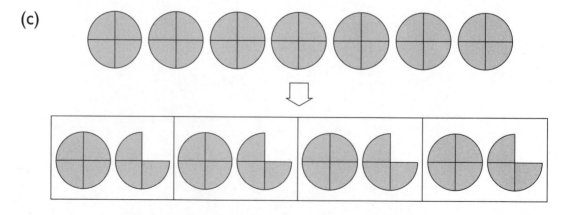

    $7 \div 4 =$

2. Change each improper fraction to a mixed number by division.

$$\frac{2}{3\overline{)8}}$$
$$\frac{6}{2}$$

$$\frac{8}{3} = 8 \div 3$$
$$=$$

$$3\overline{)10}$$

$$\frac{10}{3} = 10 \div 3$$
$$=$$

$$5\overline{)12}$$

$$\frac{12}{5} = 12 \div 5$$
$$=$$

$$4\overline{)11}$$

$$\frac{11}{4} = 11 \div 4$$
$$=$$

$$5\overline{)23}$$

$$\frac{23}{5} = 23 \div 5$$
$$=$$

$$3\overline{)20}$$

$$\frac{20}{3} = 20 \div 3$$
$$=$$

3. Change each improper fraction to a whole number or a mixed number.

(a) $\frac{8}{2} = 8 \div 2$ $\qquad 2\overline{)8}$ $=$	(b) $\frac{11}{5} = 11 \div 5$ $\qquad 5\overline{)11}$ $=$
(c) $\frac{17}{8} =$	(d) $\frac{27}{3} =$

41

EXERCISE 15

1. Add. Give each answer in its simplest form.

(a) $\dfrac{7}{8} + \dfrac{3}{4} = \dfrac{7}{8} + \dfrac{}{8}$

$=$

(b) $\dfrac{2}{3} + \dfrac{4}{9} = \dfrac{}{9} + \dfrac{4}{9}$

$=$

(c) $\dfrac{4}{5} + \dfrac{3}{10} =$

(d) $\dfrac{3}{4} + \dfrac{7}{12} =$

(e) $\dfrac{5}{6} + \dfrac{2}{3} =$

(f) $\dfrac{1}{2} + \dfrac{9}{10} =$

2. Add. Give each answer in its simplest form.

(a) $\frac{1}{6} + \frac{3}{4} = \frac{}{12} + \frac{}{12}$

$=$

(b) $\frac{5}{9} + \frac{1}{2} = \frac{}{18} + \frac{}{18}$

$=$

(c) $\frac{1}{2} + \frac{3}{5} =$

(d) $\frac{2}{5} + \frac{3}{4} =$

(e) $\frac{9}{10} + \frac{1}{6} =$

(f) $\frac{3}{10} + \frac{5}{6} =$

EXERCISE 16

1. Subtract. Give each answer in its simplest form.

(a) $\dfrac{7}{8} - \dfrac{3}{4} = \dfrac{7}{8} - \dfrac{}{8}$

$= $

(b) $\dfrac{5}{6} - \dfrac{1}{12} = \dfrac{}{12} - \dfrac{1}{12}$

$= $

(c) $\dfrac{9}{10} - \dfrac{1}{2} = $

(d) $\dfrac{11}{12} - \dfrac{2}{3} = $

(e) $1\dfrac{1}{2} - \dfrac{3}{4} = $

(f) $1\dfrac{1}{10} - \dfrac{3}{5} = $

2.   Subtract. Give each answer in its simplest form.

(a) $\dfrac{1}{2} - \dfrac{1}{5} = \dfrac{}{10} - \dfrac{}{10}$

$=$

(b) $\dfrac{7}{12} - \dfrac{3}{8} = \dfrac{}{24} - \dfrac{}{24}$

$=$

(c) $\dfrac{3}{4} - \dfrac{3}{10} =$

(d) $\dfrac{9}{10} - \dfrac{3}{4} =$

(e) $1\dfrac{1}{5} - \dfrac{2}{3} =$

(f) $1\dfrac{1}{10} - \dfrac{1}{6} =$

EXERCISE 17

1. Add. Give each answer in its simplest form.

(a) $2\frac{3}{4} + 1\frac{1}{8} = 3\frac{3}{4} + \frac{1}{8}$

$= 3\frac{}{8} + \frac{1}{8}$

$=$

(b) $1\frac{5}{12} + 3\frac{1}{3} = 4\frac{5}{12} + \frac{1}{3}$

$= 4\frac{5}{12} + \frac{}{12}$

$=$

(c) $3\frac{7}{10} + 2\frac{2}{5} =$

(d) $2\frac{2}{3} + 2\frac{5}{12} =$

(e) $3\frac{7}{12} + 1\frac{3}{4} =$

(f) $1\frac{4}{5} + 2\frac{7}{10} =$

2. Add. Give each answer in its simplest form.

(a) $2\frac{1}{5} + 1\frac{2}{3} = 3\frac{1}{5} + \frac{2}{3}$

$= 3\frac{}{15} + \frac{}{15}$

$=$

(b) $2\frac{3}{8} + 2\frac{1}{6} = 4\frac{3}{8} + \frac{1}{6}$

$= 4\frac{}{24} + \frac{}{24}$

$=$

(c) $1\frac{2}{5} + 5\frac{3}{4} =$

(d) $3\frac{1}{2} + 2\frac{7}{9} =$

(e) $2\frac{3}{10} + 2\frac{1}{6} =$

(f) $2\frac{5}{6} + 2\frac{9}{10} =$

EXERCISE 18

1. Subtract. Give each answer in its simplest form.

(a) $3\frac{7}{8} - 1\frac{1}{2} = 2\frac{7}{8} - \frac{1}{2}$

$\qquad\qquad = 2\frac{7}{8} - \frac{\ }{8}$

$\qquad\qquad =$

(b) $5\frac{4}{5} - 2\frac{1}{10} = 3\frac{4}{5} - \frac{1}{10}$

$\qquad\qquad = 3\frac{\ }{10} - \frac{\ }{10}$

$\qquad\qquad =$

(c) $4\frac{5}{6} - 2\frac{7}{12} =$

(d) $5\frac{11}{12} - 1\frac{3}{4} =$

(e) $4\frac{1}{9} - 2\frac{2}{3} =$

(f) $4\frac{1}{4} - 1\frac{5}{12} =$

2. Subtract. Give each answer in its simplest form.

(a) $4\frac{1}{2} - 1\frac{2}{9} = 3\frac{1}{2} - \frac{2}{9}$

$= 3\frac{}{18} - \frac{}{18}$

$=$

(b) $3\frac{3}{4} - 1\frac{2}{3} = 2\frac{3}{4} - \frac{2}{3}$

$= 2\frac{}{12} - \frac{}{12}$

$=$

(c) $3\frac{5}{9} - 1\frac{1}{2} =$

(d) $4\frac{7}{8} - 2\frac{5}{12} =$

(e) $4\frac{1}{4} - 2\frac{5}{6} =$

(f) $4\frac{3}{10} - 3\frac{5}{6} =$

EXERCISE 19

1. Find the equivalent measures.

(a) $\frac{5}{8}$ day = _____ h $\frac{5}{8}$ day = $\frac{5}{8} \times 24$ h =	(b) $\frac{7}{10}$ m = _____ cm
(c) $\frac{9}{20}$ min = _____ s	(d) $\frac{3}{4}$ gal = _____ qt
(e) $\frac{3}{4}$ ft = _____ in.	(f) $\frac{9}{10}$ kg = _____ g
(g) $\frac{3}{5}$ km = _____ m	(h) $\frac{5}{6}$ h = _____ min

2. Write each of the following in compound units.

(a) $2\frac{3}{5}$ m = 2 m _____ cm

$\frac{3}{5}$ m = $\frac{3}{5}$ × 100 cm

=

(b) $4\frac{7}{10}$ ℓ = 4 ℓ _____ ml

(c) $3\frac{1}{4}$ h = _____ h _____ min

(d) $2\frac{1}{2}$ days = _____ days _____ h

(e) $2\frac{2}{5}$ ℓ = _____ ℓ _____ ml

(f) $5\frac{1}{4}$ kg = _____ kg _____ g

(g) $4\frac{3}{4}$ lb = _____ lb _____ oz

(h) $3\frac{7}{8}$ km = _____ km _____ m

EXERCISE 20

1. Find the equivalent measures.

(a) $2\frac{1}{10}$ kg = _____ g
 	
  2 kg =
 	
  $\frac{1}{10}$ kg = $\frac{1}{10} \times 1000$ g
  $=$
 	
  $2\frac{1}{10}$ kg =
	(b) $1\frac{1}{6}$ h = _____ min

(c) $2\frac{2}{3}$ years = _____ months	(d) $3\frac{1}{2}$ kg = _____ g
(e) $2\frac{1}{5}$ ℓ = _____ ml	(f) $2\frac{5}{6}$ min = _____ s
(g) $4\frac{3}{5}$ m = _____ cm	(h) $3\frac{4}{5}$ km = _____ m

2. Brian jogs $3\frac{1}{8}$ km.

   Express $3\frac{1}{8}$ km in meters.

3. Peter practices on the piano for $1\frac{3}{4}$ hours.

   Pablo practices for 125 minutes.
   Who practices for a longer time? How much longer?

4. (a) Which is more, $1\frac{1}{2}$ ℓ or 1050 ml? _____

   (b) Which is longer, $1\frac{2}{3}$ h or 105 min? _____

   (c) Which is longer, $2\frac{1}{4}$ km or 2500 m? _____

   (d) Which is longer, $1\frac{1}{20}$ m or 120 cm? _____

   (e) Which is longer, $1\frac{3}{4}$ ft or 20 in.? _____

5. (a) Which is less, $1\frac{1}{4}$ ℓ or 1500 ml? _____

   (b) Which is shorter, $1\frac{1}{3}$ days or 30 h? _____

   (c) Which is shorter, $1\frac{2}{3}$ years or 18 months? _____

   (d) Which is lighter, $1\frac{4}{5}$ kg or 1400 g? _____

   (e) Which is less, $2\frac{1}{4}$ qt or 10 c? _____

53

EXERCISE 21

1. Express 8 months as a fraction of 1 year.

$$\frac{8}{12} =$$

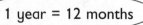 1 year = 12 months

2. Express 95 cm as a fraction of 1 m.

3. Express 45 minutes as a fraction of 1 hour.

4. Express 15 cents as a fraction of $1.

5. Express 650 g as a fraction of 1 kg.

6.	Express 40 minutes as a fraction of 2 hours.

$$\frac{40}{120} =$$

2 h = 2 × 60 min

7.	Express 8 in. as a fraction of 3 ft.

8.	What fraction of $3 is 90 cents?

9.	Mrs. King bought 2 kg of flour. She used 750 g for baking cakes.
	(a)	What fraction of the flour did she use?
	(b)	What fraction of the flour was left?

EXERCISE 22

1. Find the value of each of the following:

(a)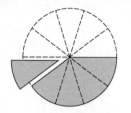

$$\frac{1}{5} \times \frac{1}{2} = \frac{1 \times 1}{5 \times 2}$$

$$=$$

$\frac{1}{5}$ of $\frac{1}{2}$ =

(b)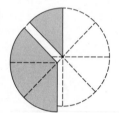

$$\frac{3}{4} \times \frac{1}{2} =$$

$\frac{3}{4}$ of $\frac{1}{2}$ =

(c)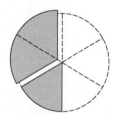

$$\frac{2}{3} \times \frac{1}{2} =$$

$\frac{2}{3}$ of $\frac{1}{2}$ =

(d)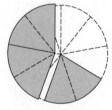

$$\frac{2}{3} \times \frac{2}{3} =$$

$\frac{2}{3}$ of $\frac{2}{3}$ =

2. Multiply.

(a) $\dfrac{4}{9} \times \dfrac{1}{2} =$

(b) $\dfrac{1}{4} \times \dfrac{3}{8} =$

(c) $\dfrac{1}{5} \times \dfrac{3}{4} =$

(d) $\dfrac{5}{6} \times \dfrac{2}{3} =$

(e) $\dfrac{4}{5} \times \dfrac{5}{8} =$

(f) $\dfrac{4}{9} \times \dfrac{3}{10} =$

(g) $\dfrac{9}{10} \times \dfrac{5}{6} =$

(h) $\dfrac{3}{8} \times \dfrac{6}{7} =$

EXERCISE 23

1. Find the answers by following the arrows.

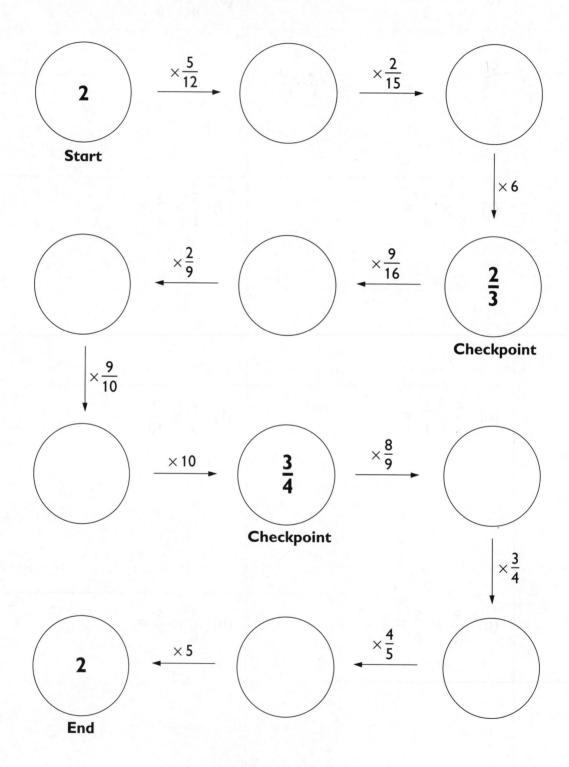

2. Mrs. Smith bought $\frac{5}{6}$ lb of meat. She cooked $\frac{2}{3}$ of it.
    How much meat did she cook?

    $$\frac{2}{3} \times \frac{5}{6} =$$

---

3. A rectangle measures $\frac{3}{4}$ yd by $\frac{2}{5}$ yd. Find its area.

---

4. Susan spent $\frac{3}{5}$ of her money on a calculator and $\frac{2}{3}$ of the remainder
    on a pen. What fraction of her money did she have left?

EXERCISE 24

1.   Find the value of each of the following:

(a) $\dfrac{1}{4} \div 2 = \dfrac{1}{4} \times \dfrac{1}{2}$

            $=$

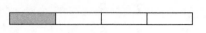

    $\dfrac{1}{2}$ of $\dfrac{1}{4} =$

(b) $\dfrac{2}{3} \div 4 = \dfrac{2}{3} \times \dfrac{1}{4}$

            $=$

    $\dfrac{1}{4}$ of $\dfrac{2}{3} =$

(c) $\dfrac{2}{3} \div 3 = \dfrac{2}{3} \times \dfrac{1}{3}$

    $\dfrac{1}{3}$ of $\dfrac{2}{3} =$

(d) $\dfrac{4}{5} \div 8 = \dfrac{4}{5} \times \dfrac{1}{8}$

            $=$

    $\dfrac{1}{8}$ of $\dfrac{4}{5} =$

2. Divide.

(a) $\frac{3}{4} \div 2 =$	(b) $\frac{8}{9} \div 4 =$
(c) $\frac{5}{6} \div 5 =$	(d) $\frac{3}{5} \div 9 =$
(e) $\frac{4}{5} \div 2 =$	(f) $\frac{5}{7} \div 6 =$
(g) $\frac{5}{8} \div 3 =$	(h) $\frac{4}{9} \div 10 =$

EXERCISE 25

1. Find the answers by following the arrows.

(a)

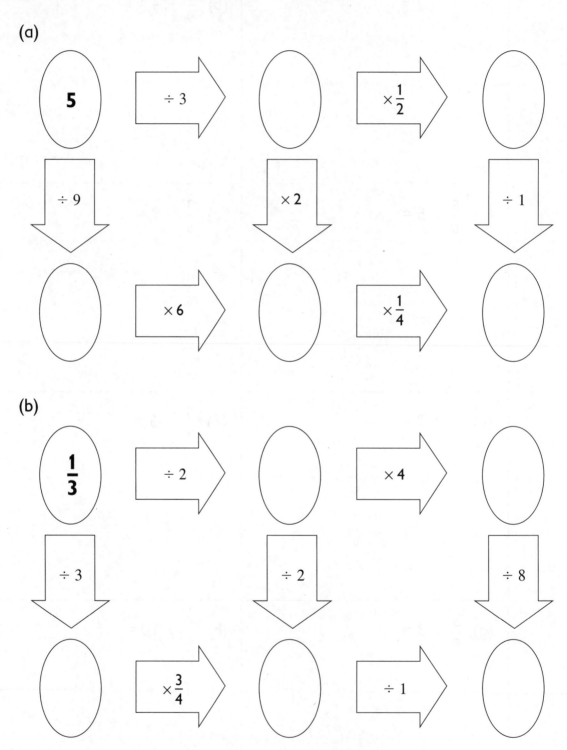

(b)

2.   Mrs. Campbell used $\frac{3}{5}$ lb of sugar in 6 days.

If she used the same amount each day, how much sugar did she use each day? Give your answer in pounds.

---

3.   A pipe of length $\frac{1}{2}$ yd is cut into 5 equal pieces.

What is the length of each piece in yards?

---

4.   Mr. Knowles had a sum of money. He kept $\frac{1}{3}$ of it and divided the rest equally among his 4 children. What fraction of the sum of money did each of his children receive?

EXERCISE 26

1. There are 50 oranges in a box. $\frac{3}{10}$ of them are rotten. How many of the oranges are **not** rotten?

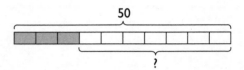

---

2. Siti spent $\frac{2}{5}$ of her money and had $60 left. How much money did she have at first?

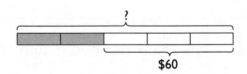

3. After spending \$30 on a dress, Mary had $\frac{3}{8}$ of her money left. How much money did she have at first?

---

4. $\frac{4}{7}$ of a group of children are boys. If there are 18 more boys than girls, how many children are there altogether?

EXERCISE 27

1. A tank is $\frac{4}{5}$ full of water. If 40 gal more water are needed to fill the tank completely, find the **capacity** of the tank.

---

2. There are 1400 students in a school. $\frac{1}{4}$ of the students wear glasses. $\frac{2}{7}$ of those who wear glasses are boys. How many boys in the school wear glasses?

3. Larry spent $\frac{1}{2}$ of his money on a camera and another $\frac{1}{8}$ on a radio. The camera cost $120 more than the radio. How much money did he have at first?

---

4. Mrs. Ricci had $480. She used $\frac{2}{3}$ of it to buy an electric fan. She also bought a tea set for $60. How much money did she have left?

EXERCISE 28

1. Tracy bought 120 eggs. She used $\frac{2}{3}$ of them for baking cakes. She used $\frac{1}{4}$ of the remainder for baking cookies. How many eggs did she have left?

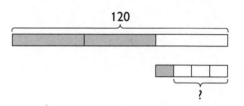

2. Mr. Ramirez had $600. He gave $\frac{3}{5}$ of it to his wife and spent $\frac{3}{8}$ of the remainder. How much did he spend?

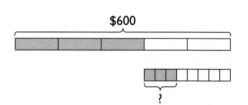

3. Lindsey made 400 tarts. She sold $\frac{3}{5}$ of them in the morning and $\frac{1}{4}$ of the remainder in the afternoon. How many tarts did she sell in the afternoon?

4. Sam packed 42 kg of rice into one big bag and 6 small ones which are of the same size. The big bag contained $\frac{3}{7}$ of the rice. How many kilograms of rice did each small bag contain?

EXERCISE 29

1. Lindsey made some tarts. She sold $\frac{3}{5}$ of them in the morning and $\frac{1}{4}$ of the remainder in the afternoon. If she had 300 tarts left, how many tarts did she make?

---

2. Mrs. Klein made some tarts. She sold $\frac{3}{5}$ of them in the morning and $\frac{1}{4}$ of the remainder in the afternoon. If she sold 200 more tarts in the morning than in the afternoon, how many tarts did she make?

3. Alex spent $\frac{1}{3}$ of his pocket money on a toy airplane and $\frac{2}{3}$ of the remainder on a toy robot. He had $20 left. How much did he spend altogether?

---

4. John spent $\frac{2}{3}$ of his money on a pen and a calculator. The calculator cost 3 times as much as the pen. If the calculator cost $24, how much money did he have left?

EXERCISE 30

1. Draw the height to the given base of each triangle.

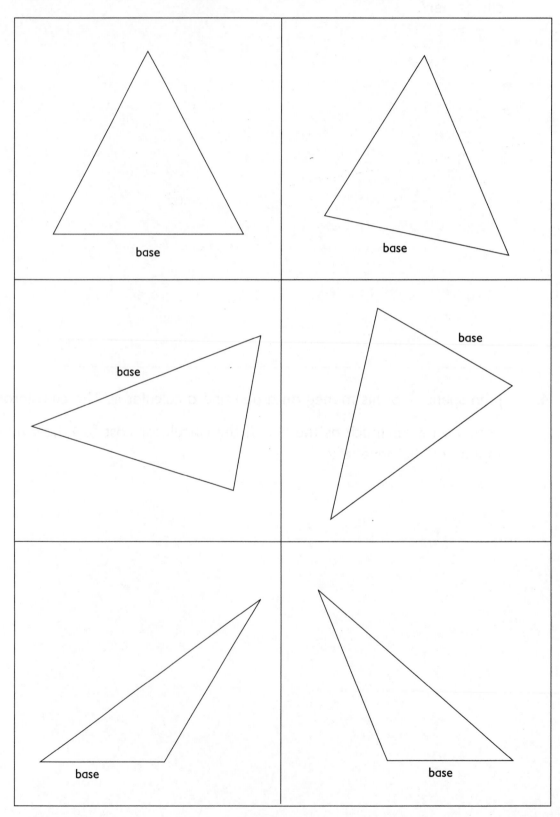

2. For each of the following triangles, name the **base** which is related to the given height.

(a)

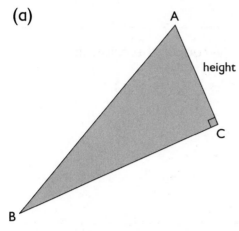

The base is _____.

(b)

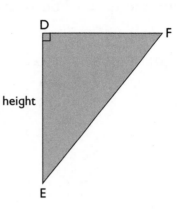

The base is _____.

(c)

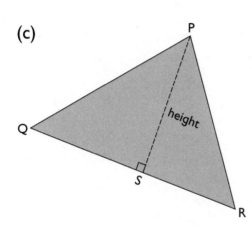

The base is _____.

(d)

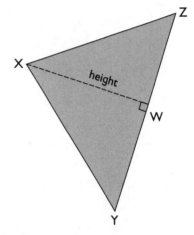

The base is _____.

(e)

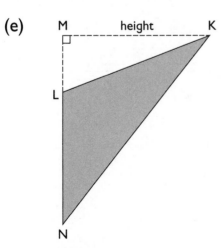

The base is _____.

(f)

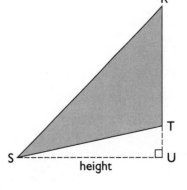

The base is _____.

EXERCISE 31

1. Find the area of each triangle.

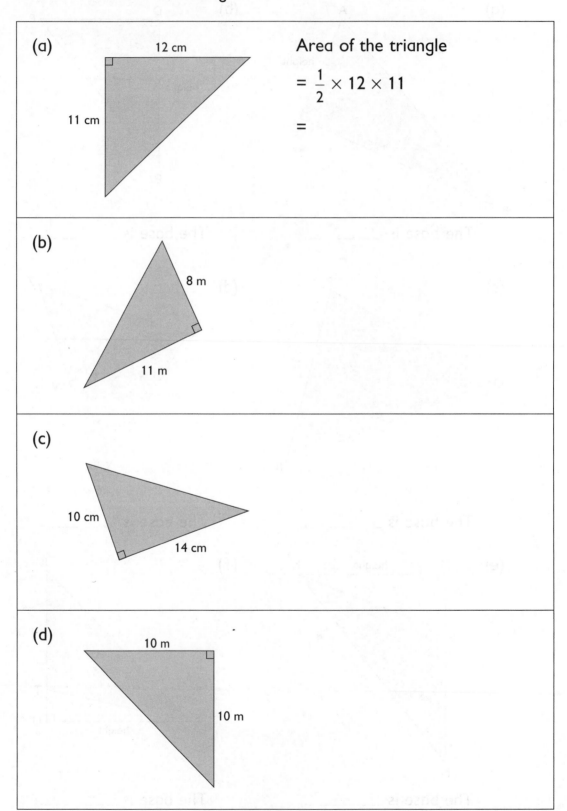

(a)

12 cm

11 cm

Area of the triangle

$= \dfrac{1}{2} \times 12 \times 11$

$=$

(b)

8 m

11 m

(c)

10 cm

14 cm

(d)

10 m

10 m

2. Find the area of each triangle.

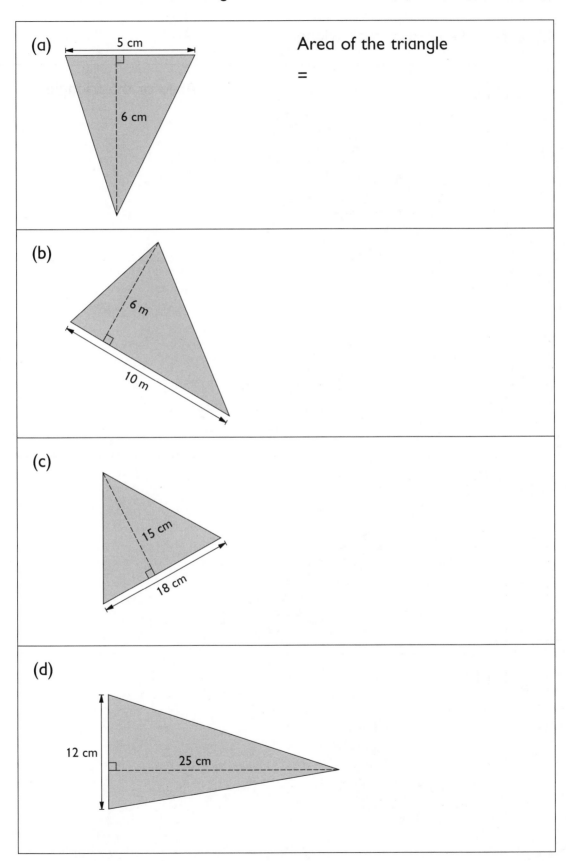

(a)

5 cm

6 cm

Area of the triangle

=

(b)

6 m

10 m

(c)

15 cm

18 cm

(d)

12 cm

25 cm

EXERCISE 32

1. Find the area of each triangle.

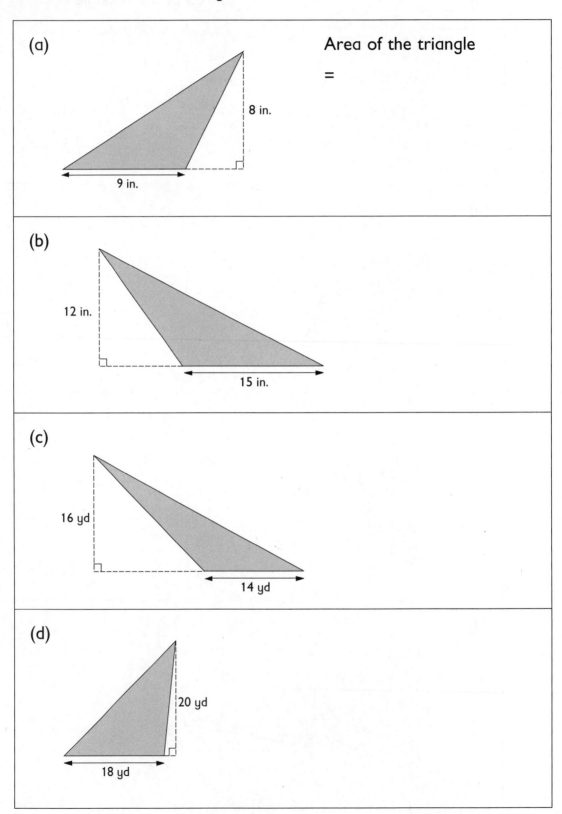

(a)

8 in.

9 in.

Area of the triangle

=

(b)

12 in.

15 in.

(c)

16 yd

14 yd

(d)

20 yd

18 yd

2. Find the area of each triangle.

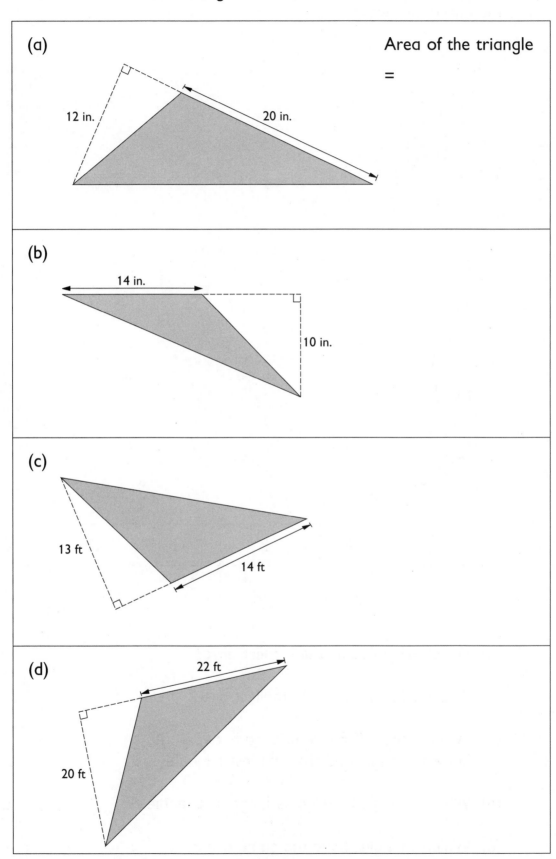

(a)

12 in.

20 in.

Area of the triangle

=

(b)

14 in.

10 in.

(c)

13 ft

14 ft

(d)

22 ft

20 ft

77

3. Find the area of each triangle. Then complete the table and answer the questions below.

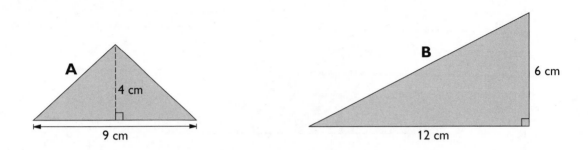

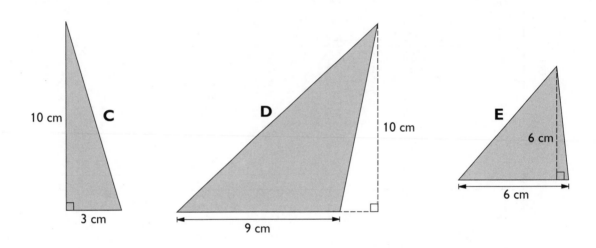

Triangle	A	B	C	D	E
Area					

(a) Which triangle has the largest area? _____

(b) Which triangle has the smallest area? _____

(c) What is the difference in area between the largest triangle and the smallest triangle? _____

(d) Which triangle is twice as large as triangle A? _____

(e) Which triangles have the same area? _____

78

EXERCISE 33

1. Find the area of each triangle.

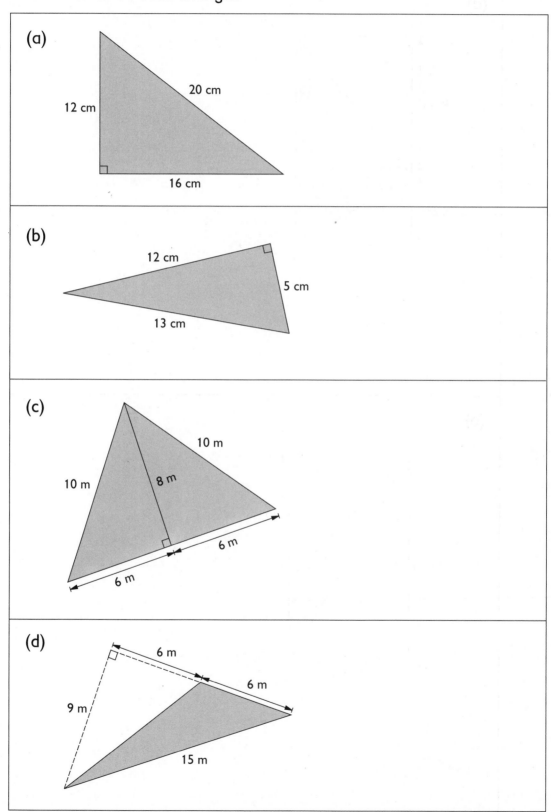

(a)

20 cm

12 cm

16 cm

(b)

12 cm

5 cm

13 cm

(c)

10 m

10 m

8 m

6 m

6 m

(d)

6 m

6 m

9 m

15 m

2. Find the shaded area of each rectangle.

(a)

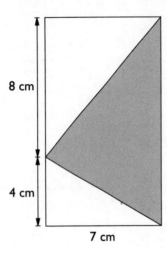

8 cm

4 cm

7 cm

(b)

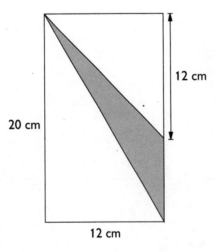

12 cm

20 cm

12 cm

(c)

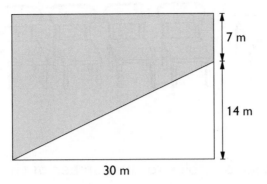

7 m

14 m

30 m

(d)

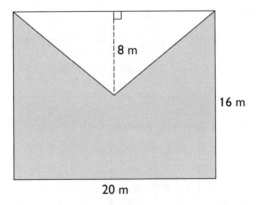

8 m

16 m

20 m

EXERCISE 34

1.

   (a) The ratio of the number of tables to the number of chairs is

         _____ : _____.

   (b) The ratio of the number of chairs to the number of tables is

         _____ : _____.

---

2.   (a) The ratio of the number of triangles
        to the number of squares is

        _____ : _____.

   (b) The ratio of the number of squares
        to the number of triangles is

        _____ : _____.

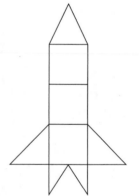

3.

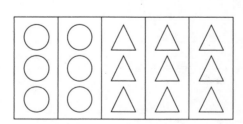

   (a) The ratio of the number of circles to the number of triangles is

         _____ : _____.

   (b) The ratio of the number of triangles to the number of circles is

         _____ : _____.

4.

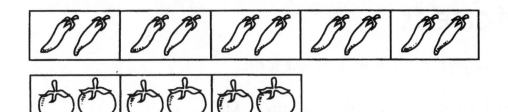

(a) The ratio of the number of peppers to the number of tomatoes is

_____ : _____.

(b) The ratio of the number of tomatoes to the number of peppers is

_____ : _____.

5.

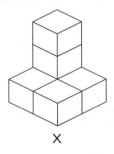

(a) The ratio of the length of Ribbon A to the length of Ribbon B is

_____ : _____.

(b) The ratio of the length of Ribbon B to the length of Ribbon A is

_____ : _____.

6.

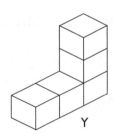

(a) The ratio of the volume of Solid X to the volume of Solid Y is

_____ : _____.

(b) The ratio of the volume of Solid Y to the volume of Solid X is

_____ : _____.

EXERCISE 35

1.   Write each ratio in its simplest form.

   (a) John saves $12 and David saves $30.
       The ratio of John's savings to David's savings is

       _____ : _____.

   (b) Mark bought 15 lb of rice and 9 lb of sugar.
       The ratio of the weight of sugar to the weight of rice is

       _____ : _____.

2.   Write each ratio in the simplest form.

6 : 9 = :	12 : 4 = :
6 : 24 = :	6 : 10 = :
25 : 15 = :	8 : 4 = :
15 : 18 = :	16 : 20 = :
20 : 40 = :	30 : 24 = :

3.   Write the missing numbers.

   (a) 2 : 1 = 10 : _____   (g) 3 : 12   = _____ : 4

   (b) 5 : 8 = 20 : _____   (h) 24 : 6   = _____ : 3

   (c) 9 : 10 = _____ : 40   (i) 2 : _____   = 8 : 16

   (d) 4 : 5   = _____ : 35   (j) 30 : _____   = 6 : 3

   (e) 9 : 3 = 3 : _____   (k) _____ : 5   = 5 : 25

   (f) 10 : 4 = 5 : _____   (l) _____ : 3   = 24 : 18

4. The length of a rectangle is 60 in. and its width is 48 in. Find the ratio of the length to the width.

5. A ribbon 40 cm long is cut into two pieces. One piece is 16 cm long. Find the ratio of the length of the longer piece to the length of the shorter piece.

6. Peter saves $52. Sumin saves $20 more than Peter. Find the ratio of Peter's savings to Sumin's savings.

EXERCISE 36

1. The ratio of the number of apples to the number of oranges is 7 : 4. There are 60 oranges. How many apples are there?

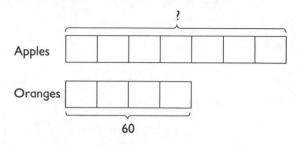

2. Sulin cuts a ribbon into two pieces in the ratio 5 : 3. The shorter piece is 42 cm long. What is the length of the original ribbon?

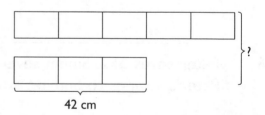

3. The ratio of the cost of a skirt to the cost of a blouse is 8 : 5. If the skirt costs $24 more than the blouse, find the cost of the blouse.

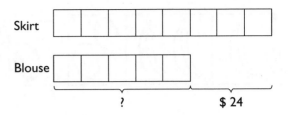

4. John and Peter shared $280 in the ratio 7 : 3. How much more money did John receive than Peter?

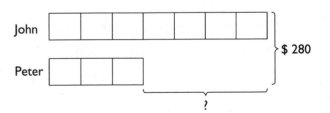

EXERCISE 37

1.

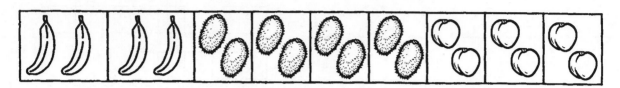

The ratio of the number of bananas to the number of kiwis to the number of apricots is _____ : _____ : _____.

2.

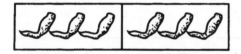

The ratio of the number of cup cakes to the number of chicken wings to the number of pastries is _____ : _____ : _____.

3.

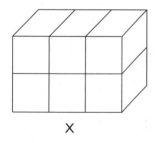

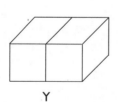

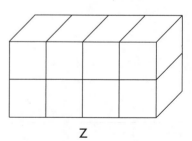

X   Y   Z

The ratio of the volume of Solid X to the volume of Solid Y to the volume of Solid Z is _____ : _____ : _____.

4.

Jim   Ravi   Rahim

Jim's weight : Ravi's weight : Rahim's weight

= _____ : _____ : _____

5.

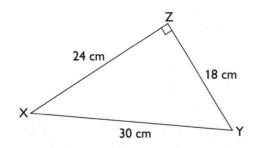

Length of XZ : Length of YZ : Length of XY

= _____ : _____ : _____

---

6.   This table shows Mingli's savings for 3 months.

January	$12
February	$12
March	$8

Savings in January : Savings in February : Savings in March

= _____ : _____ : _____

EXERCISE 38

1. A box contains blue, green and white beads. The ratio of the number of blue beads to the number of green beads to the number of white beads is 5 : 2 : 3. If there are 90 blue beads, how many beads are there altogether?

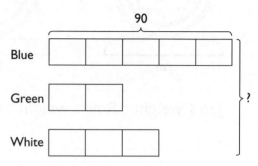

2. A piece of wire 45 cm long is bent to form a triangle. If the sides of the triangle are in the ratio 3 : 2 : 4, find the length of the longest side.

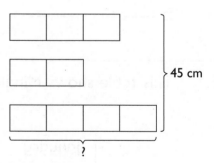

EXERCISE 39

1.   What is the size of each angle in degrees?

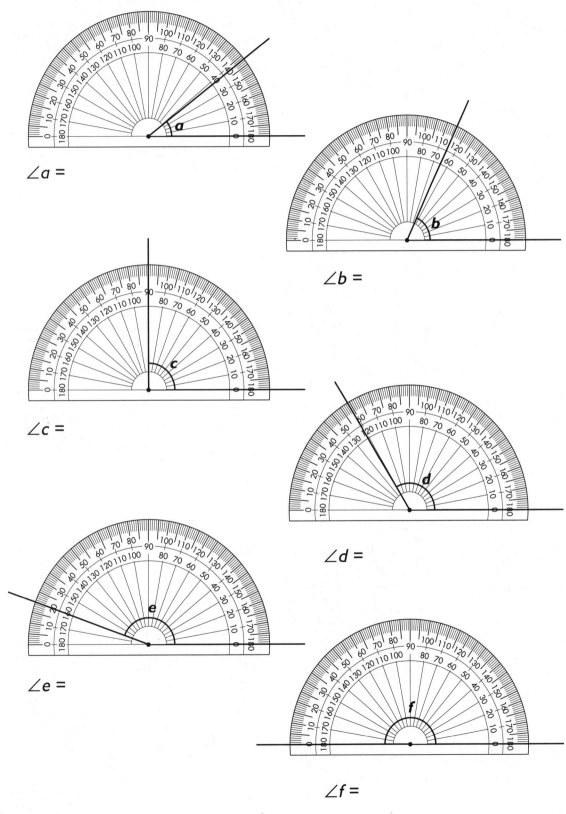

∠a =

∠b =

∠c =

∠d =

∠e =

∠f =

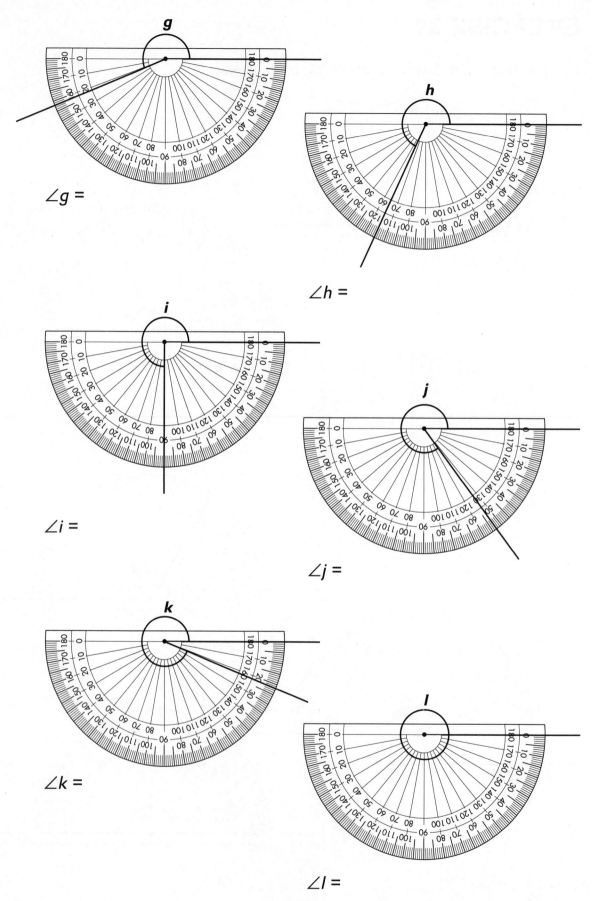

∠g =

∠h =

∠i =

∠j =

∠k =

∠l =

92

2. Estimate and then measure the marked angles.

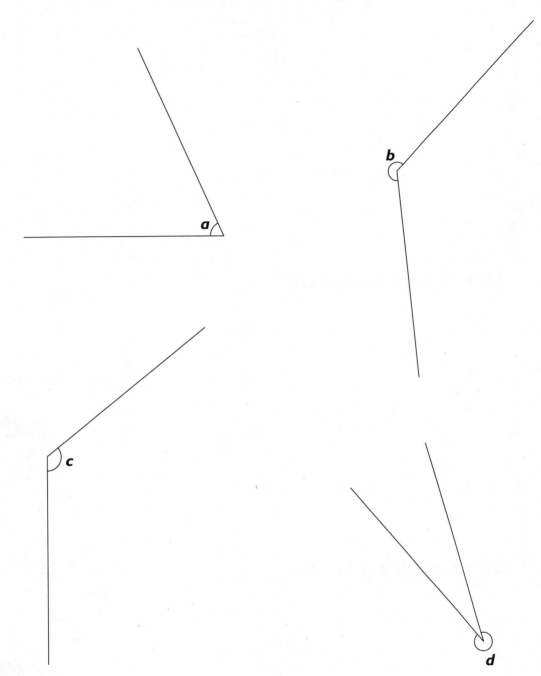

Angle	*a*	*b*	*c*	*d*
Estimate				
Measure				

3.   Draw an angle equal to 165°.

4.   Draw an angle equal to 250°.

5.   Draw an angle equal to 325°.

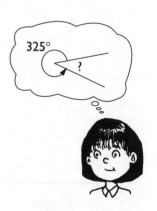

EXERCISE 40

1.

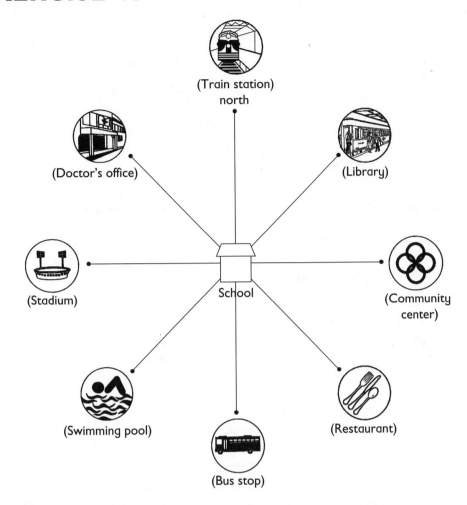

(Train station)
north

(Doctor's office)

(Library)

(Stadium)

School

(Community center)

(Swimming pool)

(Bus stop)

(Restaurant)

In which direction is each place from the school?
Complete the following table:

Place	Direction from school
Train station	north
Bus stop	
Library	
Restaurant	
Stadium	
Doctor's office	
Community center	
Swimming pool	

2.

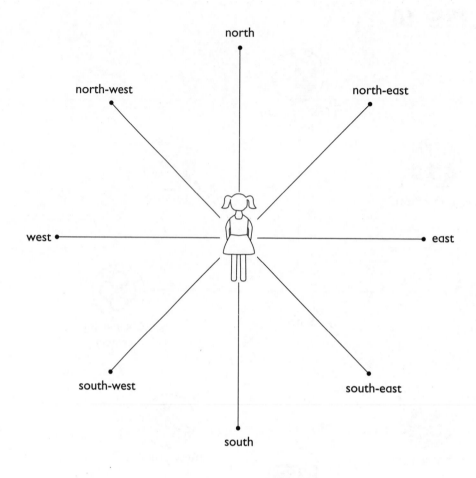

Complete the following table:

I am facing	If I turn	I will be facing
north	45° clockwise	
south	90° counterclockwise	
north-west	180° clockwise	
east	135° counterclockwise	
south-east	clockwise	south
north-east	clockwise	south-east
south-east	counterclockwise	north
west	clockwise	north-west

EXERCISE 41

1.   The following figures are not drawn to scale.
     Find the unknown marked angles.

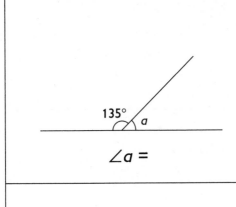

135°

a

∠a =

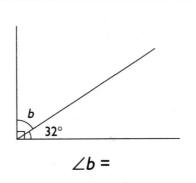

b   32°

∠b =

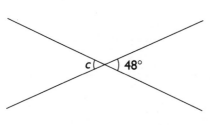

c   48°

∠c =

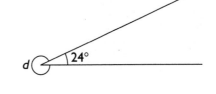

24°   d

∠d =

e

250°

∠e =

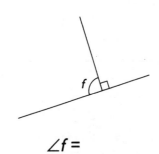

f

∠f =

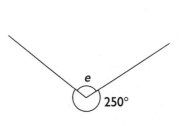

g

28°

∠g =

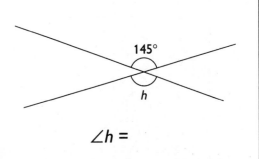

145°

h

∠h =

2. The following figures are not drawn to scale.
Find the unknown marked angles.

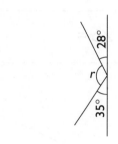

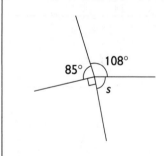

REVIEW 2

Write the answers in the boxes.

1. Replace 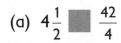 by the symbols for **greater than (>), less than (<)** or **equal to (=)**.

    (a) $4\frac{1}{2}$ 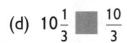 $\frac{42}{4}$

    (b) $3\frac{1}{7}$ ▆ $\frac{31}{7}$

    (c) $\frac{34}{8}$ ▆ $4\frac{1}{4}$

    (d) $10\frac{1}{3}$ ▆ $\frac{10}{3}$

2. Find the value of each of the following:

    (a) $2\frac{3}{8} + \frac{7}{12}$

    (b) $4\frac{1}{3} - 1\frac{8}{9}$

    (c) $\frac{7}{9} \times \frac{3}{4}$

    (d) $36 \times \frac{5}{9}$

3. Write the missing numbers.

    (a) $4\frac{1}{2}$ h = ☐ h ☐ min

    (b) $2\frac{1}{4}$ years = ☐ years ☐ months

    (c) $3\frac{9}{10}$ m = ☐ m ☐ cm

    (d) $5\frac{3}{10}$ kg = ☐ kg ☐ g

99

4. (a) Which is longer, $\frac{4}{5}$ m or 85 cm?

   (b) Which is longer, $1\frac{2}{3}$ years or 17 months?

   (c) Which is heavier, $2\frac{1}{10}$ kg or 2001 g?

   (d) Which is more, 350 ml or 3 liters 50 ml?

5. What fraction of the figure is shaded?

6. If the square has the same perimeter as the rectangle, find the area of the square.

6 yd

12 yd

7. If 2 liters of a liquid weigh 600 g, then 3 liters of the liquid weigh

   g.

8. Lihua bought 5 packets of white envelopes and 3 packets of brown envelopes. There were 112 envelopes in each packet. How many envelopes did she buy altogether?

9. Robert packed 1320 cookies into packets of 22 each. He sold all the cookies at $2 per packet. How much money did he make?

10. Lily has been working for $6\frac{1}{4}$ years and Susan has been working for $2\frac{1}{2}$ years. Lily has been working   years   months longer than Susan.

11. 64 children attended a computer course. $\frac{5}{8}$ of them were girls. How many more girls than boys were there?

12. The length and the width of a rectangle are in the ratio 5 : 3. The length of the rectangle is 20 in.

   (a) Find its width.

   (b) Find its area.

   (c) Find its perimeter.

13. The sides of a triangle are in the ratio 5 : 2 : 4.
   The longest side of the triangle is 15 cm.
   (a) Find its shortest side.

   (b) Find its perimeter.

14. In each of the following figures, not drawn to scale, find ∠x.

   (a)

   (b)

   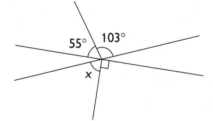

15. What fraction of the rectangle is shaded?

   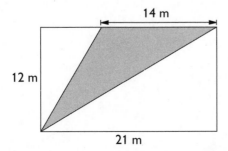

101

16. The ratio of Gary's weight to Andy's weight is 4 : 5. Their total weight is 117 kg.
    (a) Find Andy's weight.

    (b) Find Gary's weight.

17. The ratio of the height of a tree to the length of its shadow is 3 : 2. The height of the tree is 15 m. Find the length of its shadow.

18. Arrange the numbers in decreasing order.

    $\dfrac{9}{4}$, $2\dfrac{1}{12}$, $2\dfrac{1}{2}$, $\dfrac{12}{11}$

19. Which one of the following is nearest to 4?

    $3\dfrac{1}{8}$, $3\dfrac{11}{12}$, $4\dfrac{9}{10}$, $4\dfrac{4}{5}$

20. Find the shaded area of each of the rectangles.

    (a)

    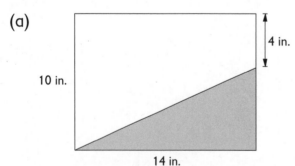

    10 in.

    4 in.

    14 in.

    (b)

    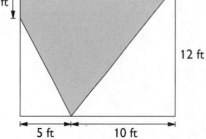

    3 ft

    12 ft

    5 ft   10 ft

    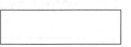

21. The area of the shaded part is $\frac{1}{3}$ of the area of the rectangle. Find the area of the rectangle.

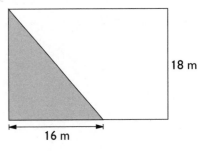

22. Ali sold 5 oven toasters and 3 rice cookers for $500. If a rice cooker cost $20 less than an oven toaster, find the cost of a rice cooker.

23. The ratio of Bill's money to Henry's money was 5 : 6. After Bill spent $800 on a TV set, the ratio became 1 : 2. How much money did Henry have?

---

24. The area of the square is the same as the area of the triangle. Find the perimeter of the square.

 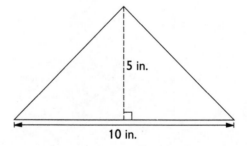

10 in.